GREEN WORLD

ORCHIDS

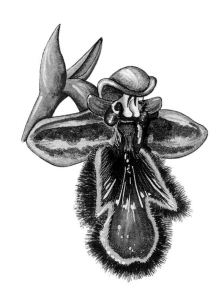

Written by
Deni Bown

HEINEMANN

A Templar Book
First published in Great Britain in 1991
by Heinemann Children's Reference,
a division of Heinemann Educational Books Ltd
Halley Court, Jordan Hill, Oxford OX2 8JE
Devised and produced by The Templar Company plc
Pippbrook Mill, London Road, Dorking, Surrey RH4 1JE
Copyright © 1991 by The Templar Company plc

Editor: Wendy Madgwick
Designer: Jane Hunt
Illustrator: Sallie Reason
Consultant: John Blowers

Colour separations by Chroma Graphics, Singapore
Printed and bound by L.E.G.O., Vicenza, Italy

British Library Cataloguing in Publication Data
Bown, Deni
Orchids
1. Orchids
I. Title   II. Series
584.15

ISBN 0-431-00849-3

Notes to reader
There are some words in this book which are printed in **bold** type.
A brief explanation of these words is given in the glossary on p. 44.

All living things are given two Latin names when first classified by a
scientist. Some of them also have a common name, for example pansy
orchid, *Miltonia spectabilis*. In this book, the common name is used
where possible, but the scientific name is given when first mentioned.

Photographic credits
t = top, b = bottom, l = left, r = right
Cover: John Blowers; page 10*l* Deni Bown; page 10*r* Bruce Coleman/E.
Crichton; page 13 Paul Davis; page 15 Bruce Coleman/J. Shaw; page 16
John Blowers; page 19 John Blowers; page 21 Deni Bown; page 22
Bruce Coleman/C.B. and D.W. Frith; page 28 Bruce Coleman/E.
Crichton; page 30 David Leigh; page 33*r* Frank Lane/K.G. Preston
Mafham; page 33*l* Bruce Coleman/F. Sauer; page 35 Royal Botanic
Gardens, Edinburgh; page 36 Royal Botanic Gardens, Edinburgh; page
37*t* Trustees of Chatsworth House; page 37*b,l* John Blowers; page 37*b,r*
Eric Crichton; page 38 Bruce Coleman/Roger Wilmhurst; page 40 John
Blowers; page 42 Harry Smith Collection.

CONTENTS

GREEN WORLD

This tree shows the different groups of plants that are found in the world. It does not show how they developed or their relationship with each other.

MONOCOTYLEDONS

DICOTYLEDONS

FLOWERING PLANTS (Angiosperms)

CONIFEROUS (OR FIR) TREES (Gymnosperms)

FERNS, CLUBMOSSES AND HORSETAILS (Pteridophytes)

MOSSES AND LIVERWORTS (Bryophytes)

ALGAE

GREEN PLANTS

PLANTS

ANIMALS

FUNGI AND LICHENS

BACTERIA

SLIME MOULDS

LIVING THINGS

Group 1: Pondweeds; water plantains
■ Most have narrow leaves and small flowers
■ They grow in or under water

Group 2: Grasses; bamboos; rushes; reeds; sedges
■ They have narrow leaves and spikes of tiny flowers
■ Their seeds are filled with starch

Group 3: Pineapples
■ Short-stemmed plants with a rosette of stiff, narrow leaves
■ The flower spike consists of small flowers and coloured bracts

Group 4: Palms; screwpines; Panama hat plants
■ Most have a crown of leaves at the top of a thick trunk
■ The leaves are feather – or fan-shaped

Group 5: Bananas; gingers; arrowroots
■ Most have oval leaves with stalks that wrap round the stem
■ The large showy flowers are in spikes

Group 6: Arums; Swiss cheese plants; philodendrons
■ Leaves may be narrow or compound and the veins form a network
■ The flowers are usually hidden inside a large bract – the spathe

Group 7: Lilies; irises; onions; daffodils
■ Most have grass-like or sword-shaped leaves

Group 8: Orchids
■ Leaves are narrow or ovate (egg-shaped)
■ The flowers have three petals and three sepals; one petal forms a lip
■ The seeds are tiny and have no food reserves

The land area of the world is divided into 10 main zones depending on the plants that grow there. Orchids grow in all zones except in the driest deserts, coldest Arctic regions and the tops of high mountains.

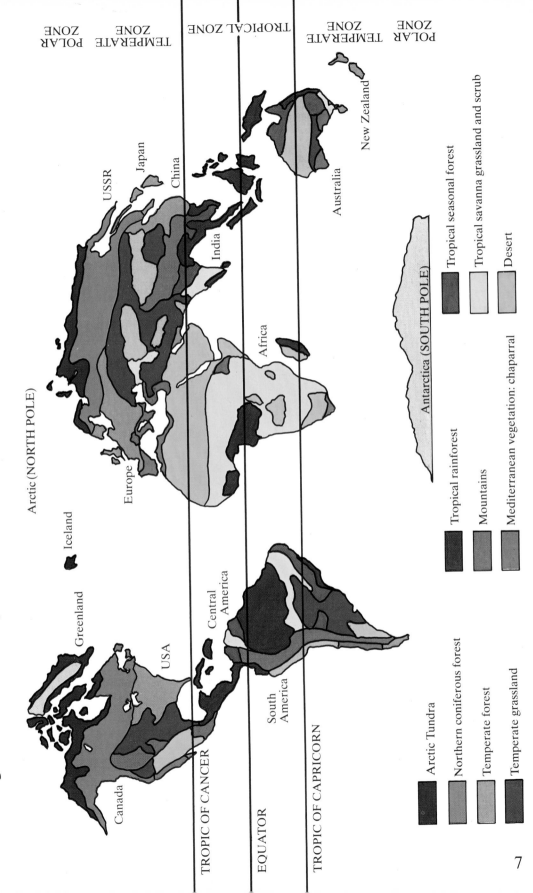

POLAR ZONE — TEMPERATE ZONE — TROPICAL ZONE — TROPICAL ZONE — TEMPERATE ZONE — POLAR ZONE

Arctic (NORTH POLE)

USSR
Japan
China
India
Europe
Africa
Iceland
Greenland
USA
Central America
Canada
South America
Australia
New Zealand

Antarctica (SOUTH POLE)

TROPIC OF CANCER
EQUATOR
TROPIC OF CAPRICORN

Arctic Tundra
Northern coniferous forest
Temperate forest
Temperate grassland

Tropical rainforest
Mountains
Mediterranean vegetation: chaparral

Tropical seasonal forest
Tropical savanna grassland and scrub
Desert

ORCHIDS

Orchids belong to the major group of plants called **angiosperms** or flowering plants (see p. 6 and p. 26). There are about 350 families of flowering plants on the Earth. Each family is divided into large groups called **genera**. Each group or **genus** consists of one or more kinds or **species** of flowering plant. Orchids belong to a family known as Orchidaceae. It is the largest family of flowering plants, with about 750 genera and around 25,000 species.

All orchids have similar features. Their leaves are undivided and narrow or ovate (egg-shaped). They alternate on the stem, often in two rows, and the veins run in straight lines down the leaf. The flowers have three **sepals** and three **petals** (see p. 26). One of the petals is quite different from the other two. It is called the **lip** and is often larger or more brightly coloured. The **pollen** grains of orchids are not loose and powdery, as in most flowering plants, but join together to form waxy masses called **pollinia** (see p. 26). Orchid **seeds** are produced in a pod or capsule (see p. 30). They are so small that they look like powder.

Long lives
Most orchids are perennials and live for many years. They are found throughout the world. They vary a great deal in size and form.

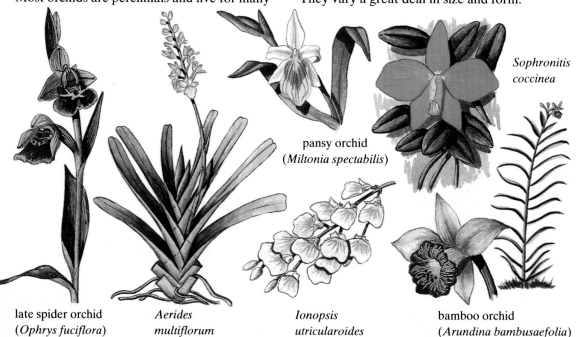

Sophronitis
coccinea

pansy orchid
(*Miltonia spectabilis*)

late spider orchid
(*Ophrys fuciflora*)

Aerides multiflorum

Ionopsis utricularoides

bamboo orchid
(*Arundina bambusaefolia*)

8

What's it called?

Many plants have one or more common names, such as slipper orchid or lady's slipper. Quite different plants can have the same common name. For example, there are several different orchids that are known as butterfly orchids. This can be confusing when you are trying to identify a plant or talk about it, especially when the common name is in a foreign language. For this reason, botanists (people who study plants) give each species a scientific name in Latin. Whatever region or country the plant grows in, the scientific name stays the same. A scientific name has two parts: a genus name followed by a species name. Botanists have to classify a plant before it is given a scientific name. This means deciding which family it belongs to and which are its closest relatives.

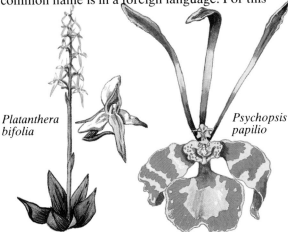

Platanthera bifolia

Psychopsis papilio

Both of these plants are known as butterfly orchids but they belong to different genera.

Cypripedium calceolus   *Cypripedium acaule*

The scientific name of the yellow lady's slipper is *Cypripedium calceolus*. A close relative is the pink lady's slipper, *Cypripedium acaule.*

Bulbophyllum minutissimum from Australia is a few millimetres tall with flowers no bigger than a pin head.

Grammatophyllum speciosum from Malaysia is over 7 metres tall with flowers 15 centimetres across.

■ Orchids are angiosperms or flowering plants.
■ They are monocotyledons with only one seed leaf.
■ The veins in the leaves run in straight lines down the leaves.
■ One of the petals forms a distinct lip.
■ The pollen grains form a waxy mass – the pollinia.
■ The seeds are very tiny and contained in a pod or capsule.

WHERE ORCHIDS GROW

Like all flowering plants, orchids need water, light, warmth and nutrients (food) to grow. If you look at the map on page 7 you will see that the Earth's surface is divided into 10 main zones. Each zone provides different growing conditions. The orchid family is so adaptable that it has members in parts of each zone. However, most orchids can only live in one area or **habitat** and are found nowhere else.

Grassland orchids
Grasslands occur in temperate and tropical regions. There is little shade in grassland, so orchids in these habitats are specially adapted to living in very light places.

Green-winged orchids (*Orchis morio*, above left) grow in large groups in the short grass of temperate meadows in Europe. The tall grasses of tropical America help to support the reed-like stems of *Epidendrum ibaguense* (above right).

Arctic orchids
The lesser twayblade (*Listera cordata*, shown above) grows north of the Arctic Circle in North America, Greenland, Europe and Asia. It grows, flowers and sets seed quickly, dying down and surviving the winter as underground stems.

Rainforest orchids
Rainforest orchids grow high up on the trunks and branches of trees and shrubs. Orchids that perch on other plants are called **epiphytes** (see p. 34-35).

Woodland orchids
Purple helleborines (*Epipactis purpurata*) grow throughout Europe in temperate woodland. They grow slowly in the shade of beech trees and flower from August to September.

Salt-water orchids
Salt water kills most flowering plants. Some orchids are specially adapted to sea water or salt-laden winds. In Florida, *Epidendrum boothianum* (shown above) can be found as an epiphyte in mangrove swamps and other kinds of orchid grow in tidal areas.

Bog orchids
Many temperate and tropical orchids grow in the waterlogged soils of bogs and marshes. The broad-leaved marsh orchid (*Dactylorhiza majalis*, shown above) grows in European marshes. The grass pink (*Calopogon pulchellus*) is found in swamps in Florida, Cuba and the Bahamas.

Desert and dune orchids
Some orchids can grow in very dry conditions. The flying ducks orchid (*Caleana nigrita*, shown above) grows in the Australian bush. Certain helleborine orchids grow in sand dunes in north-west Europe. In the driest months they survive underground as **tubers** (swollen stems or roots).

ORCHIDS OF EUROPE

There are about 200 different kinds of orchid in Europe, and they are found in every habitat – woodlands, grasslands, mountains and even in the Arctic tundra. All of them are terrestrial (ground-dwelling). In southern Europe, around the Mediterranean, the growing season is from late autumn to spring, when it is cool and rainy. Mediterranean orchids die down and remain **dormant** (resting) during the hot, dry summer. The best time to find Mediterranean orchids flowering is from March to May.

In northern Europe, orchids are dormant during the cold winter and start growing again in the warm, wet spring. Most orchids in northern Europe flower from June to August.

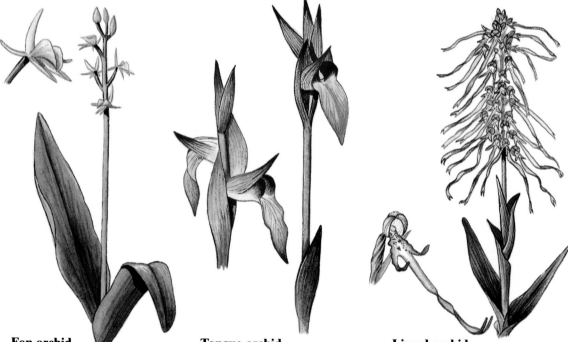

Fen orchid
(*Liparis loeselii*)
This orchid is hard to find because it is so small. Its tiny green flowers grow on stalks only 6 – 20 centimetres tall. It is also rare as it grows only in marshy, low-lying areas, known as fens. Most fens have now been drained for farming.

Tongue orchid
(*Serapias lingua*)
This orchid is between 10 and 30 centimetres tall and grows in damp, grassy and sandy places. The flower spike has up to eight flowers which vary from pale pink to dark reddish-pink. The lip is large and shaped like a tongue.

Lizard orchid
(*Himantoglossum hircinum*)
The lizard orchid is the largest European orchid. It can grow up to 90 centimetres and bears 15 to 80 flowers. The flowers are about 6 centimetres long and have tail-shaped lips. It is also called the goat orchid, because of the flowers' smell.

12

Adam and Eve orchids

The elder-flowered orchid (*Dactylorhiza sambucina*) is one of the few yellow-flowered European orchids. It is found in central and southern Europe and in parts of Scandinavia, growing in woods and meadows on the sides of mountains, up to 2000 metres. The flowers are usually yellow but sometimes pink. In some places where the two colours grow together, it is called the Adam and Eve orchid (see right).

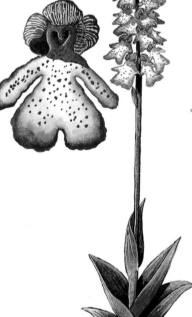

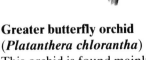

Bee orchid
(*Ophrys apifera*)

Bee orchids grow mainly in dry grassy places and are 15 – 50 centimetres tall. The flowers usually have pink sepals, two very small green petals and a large velvety brown lip that looks like a bumble bee.

Lady orchid
(*Orchis purpurea*)

The flowers look like ladies in wide skirts. Lady orchids grow mainly in woods on chalk or limestone soils. They are found all round the Mediterranean and in central Europe, but are rare in the north.

Greater butterfly orchid
(*Platanthera chlorantha*)

This orchid is found mainly in chalk or limestone grassland, often among bushes or at the edge of a wood. It is up to 50 centimetres tall, with scented greenish-white flowers.

NORTH AMERICAN ORCHIDS

North America stretches from the arctic regions of Canada and the United States to the tropical swamps of Florida. It has about 200 different orchids, growing in various habitats. Orchids in the far north are similar to those in arctic regions of Europe, but species in the warm southern states are more like those in tropical America.

Most North American orchids are terrestrial, but the states that border on the Gulf of Mexico, like Florida, are warm and wet enough for epiphytes. The only epiphytic orchid to grow outside Florida is the green-fly orchid (*Epidendrum conopseum*), which is found throughout the Gulf states and into Mexico.

Some orchids that were brought from other countries into warm parts of the USA have become weeds. One particular kind of Asian orchid, which has leafy stems and dense spikes of white flowers, probably reached Florida with imported grass seed. It soon appeared in many neighbouring states. In Hawaii, another Asian orchid has spread widely throughout the countryside.

**Venus slipper
(*Calypso bulbosa*)**
This small plant, only 10 – 20 centimetres tall, is found in damp, mossy coniferous woods in the Rocky Mountains. Each plant produces one oval leaf, followed by a single flower which smells of vanilla.

**Rattlesnake plantain
(*Goodyera pubescens*)**
This woodland orchid is found throughout USA. It reaches about 35 centimetres tall and has tiny white flowers. The leaves are unusual for an orchid as they have a network of silvery-white veins.

**Whorled pogonia
(*Isotria verticillata*)**
This woodland orchid reaches 30 centimetres tall and produces large single flowers above a whorl of leaves. It is found in eastern states of the USA, from Maine to Georgia.

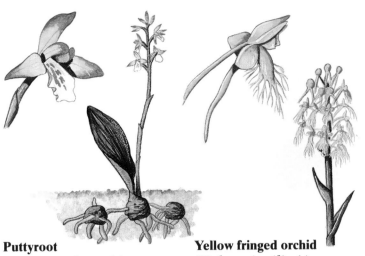

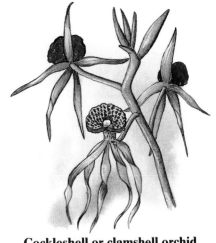

Puttyroot
(*Aplectrum hyemale*)
This odd orchid is the only one in the genus *Aplectrum*. It produces a chain of tubers which have a sticky juice. It grows in an unusual way. It produces a single leaf in the autumn which dies down in the spring before the flowers are produced.

Yellow fringed orchid
(*Habenaria ciliaris*)
About 500 species of *Habenaria* grow in boggy places. Most have tubers and a pair of ovate leaves. In many the flowers have a fringed lip. This species is found from north-east Canada to Florida in the USA and reaches over 1 metre tall.

Cockleshell or clamshell orchid
(*Encyclia cochleata*)
This tropical epiphyte grows in Florida and south into Brazil. It has upside-down flowers with a blackish-purple lip shaped like a shell. Easy to grow, it first flowered in cultivation at the Royal Botanic Gardens, Kew, England in 1787.

Lady's slipper
North America has about a dozen different species of *Cypripedium*. They grow in moist woods and have creeping **rhizomes** (swollen underground stems), pleated leaves and pouched flowers. Showy lady's slipper (*Cypripedium reginae*) pictured on the left is the state flower of Minnesota. It grows in large numbers around the Great Lakes, between Canada and the United States.

CENTRAL & SOUTH AMERICA

The American tropics have more kinds of orchid than anywhere else on Earth. Some species of orchids are terrestrial (ground-dwelling) but over 80 per cent grow as epiphytes on trees or rocks in forests.

Tropical orchids are common in lowland rainforests, such as those along the Amazon river, but there are even greater numbers in the cooler montane forests that grow on the sides of mountains. The richest areas of all are in the Andes, a chain of high mountains that runs for about 7250 kilometres down the western side of South America. Colombia, a country at the northern end of the Andes, has over 2000 species of orchids.

Although orchids are much more common in tropical forests than in temperate woods, most are quite rare. Some grow only in one particular area; others are widely scattered over a very large region. They are also more difficult to see as they grow high up in trees.

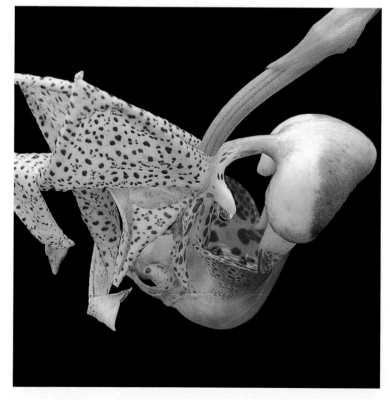

Bucket orchids
In tropical American bucket orchids (*Coryanthes*, see right) the lip forms a container that fills with liquid. The rim of the "bucket" is coated with a scented oil that attracts bees. As the bee busily collects the oil, it slips and falls into the liquid. Just as it is beginning to drown, the bee finds the only way out – a narrow tunnel. As it struggles through, the pollinia become glued to its back (see pp. 26-28).

Cattleya dowiana

Most cattleyas have slender **pseudobulbs** (thickened part of the stem), each with one or two leathery leaves and large, brightly coloured flowers. This species is from Costa Rica and Colombia but is now very rare. Its magnificent scented flowers measure 20 centimetres across.

Clown or tiger orchid (*Rossioglossum grande*)

This orchid grows in the mountains of Mexico and Guatemala. It has 4 – 8 large flowers which appear only after a period of cold, dry weather. The petals are striped and the central body or **column** of the flower looks like a clown.

Dracula chimaera

This strange orchid is found in Colombia. Its hairy flowers have very small lips and the three sepals narrow into tails that measure almost 18 centimetres long. The flower stalks grow out at right angles to the plant so that the flowers hang face-downwards.

Lady-of-the-night (*Brassavola nodosa*)

This orchid grows as an epiphyte in mangrove swamps, on large cacti and on trees and cliffs in Central America, as far south as Peru. The flowers open at night and give out a sweet soapy scent which attracts moths.

Lynx or horned orchid (*Stanhopea tigrina*)

This epiphytic Mexican species has egg-shaped pseudobulbs, broad leaves and flower stalks that hang straight down. The huge, waxy flowers smell strongly of vanilla and over-ripe fruit.

Cradle or tulip orchid (*Anguloa clowesii*)

Anguloa orchids grow in the Andes. This one is found at 1800 metres in Colombia. It has large leaves, and fragrant cup-shaped flowers. In dry, cool weather the leaves fall and the plant survives as pseudobulbs, flowering before growth begins.

ORCHIDS OF AFRICA

Africa is mostly tropical, apart from the extreme north and south which are temperate. Northern Africa borders on the Mediterranean and its orchids are more like those of southern Europe. The southern tip of South Africa has a similar climate to the north, with hot, dry summers and cool, rainy winters, but the orchids are quite different. Like all temperate species, they are terrestrial and die down for several months of the year. South Africa alone has about 550 species.

Much of Africa is covered in desert and tropical grasslands, where there are few orchids. The rest has a variety of vegetation zones, including a broad belt of rainforest that runs from the centre of the continent to the west coast. The orchids there are mostly epiphytes.

The island of Madagascar (the Malagasy Republic) is over 1600 kilometres long and lies off the east coast of Africa. Its tropical forests have many orchids that are found nowhere else.

**Leopard orchid
(*Ansellia africana*)**
The leopard orchid is found right across Africa, varying in flower size and colour from east to west. It makes a stout plant with stems up to 2 metres tall and large sprays of brown-spotted flowers.

Aërangis rhodosticta
There are about 70 different kinds of *Aërangis* in tropical Africa and Madagascar. Most produce graceful arching spikes of pale flowers. This species grows as an epiphyte in the montane forests of central and east Africa.

Eulophia guineensis
This is a terrestrial orchid from the tropical savanna grasslands of central Africa. It dies down during the cool, dry months. When the rainy season starts, it sends up new leaves and an upright spike of pink-lipped flowers.

Fishy flowers

Bulbophyllum is the largest genus of orchids, with over 1000 species. Many have small, rather peculiar flowers that smell unpleasant. The flowers of *Bulbophyllum barbigerum* from west Africa (see left) smell like rotting fish. The lip is covered with fine hairs and is delicately hinged. The hairs move in the breeze and the whole lip bobs up and down, wafting the smell to attract insects.

Cymbidiella rhodochila

Some epiphytic orchids prefer certain kinds of trees. This *Cymbidiella* is usually found on acacia trees, growing next to epiphytic staghorn ferns. It is a rare orchid, found only on the island of Madagascar.

Pride of Table Mountain (*Disa uniflora*)

Disa grows on rocky ledges and along streams in the mountains of South Africa. The scarlet flower is triangular in shape, with very large sepals. The lip and petals are extremely small.

Herschelia charpenteriana

The odd flowers of this rare ground orchid have dangling lips about 6.5 centimetres long. It grows in the south-west Cape of South Africa, an area known for its great variety of orchids and other wild flowers.

NORTH AND EAST ASIA

Northern and eastern Asia includes China, Korea, Japan, Tibet, Nepal, Bhutan, northern India, Burma and part of the Soviet Union. The Himalayan mountains run through the centre of the region. The area is divided between temperate and tropical zones. There are hardy or cool-growing terrestrial orchids to the north and on the lower slopes of the mountains, and tropical species to the south and in the warmer valleys.

Islands often have different kinds of plants from the mainland, because seeds do not spread easily across the sea. Japan consists of a chain of islands that stretch for almost 3000 kilometres off the coast of north-east Asia. The islands are mountainous and there are warm currents in the surrounding sea. This gives Japan a varied climate and a wide range of vegetation zones. Epiphytic orchids grow in the southernmost island of Kyushu.

Cymbidium hookerianum
Cymbidium orchids can be terrestrial or epiphytic. They mostly have long strap-shaped leaves and sturdy spikes of large flowers. This Himalayan species grows as an epiphyte at 1500 – 2000 metres in India, Nepal and Tibet.

**Slipper orchid
(*Paphiopedilum venustum*)**
This orchid grows as a terrestrial plant in the Himalayan foothills of Nepal, Bhutan and India. It flowers during the cool, dry season and new leaves form when the warm monsoon rains begin.

**Himalayan lady's slipper
(*Cypripedium himalaicum*)**
This lady's slipper orchid grows at 2400 – 3900 metres in the western Himalayas. Other relatives include species that grow in the USA (see p. 15), Tibet, Japan, the Soviet Union and China.

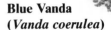

Windowsill orchid
(***Pleione bulbocodioides***)

Pleione orchids grow in the mountains. This species, found in Tibet, China and Taiwan, can be grown in pots on a windowsill. They all have small pseudobulbs and grow as epiphytes on trees and rocks.

Neofinetia falcata

The only species in the genus *Neofinetia*, this night-scented epiphyte is found in warm parts of Japan, China and Korea. It is grown as a house plant in these countries. Plants with yellow-striped leaves are especially popular.

Blue Vanda
(***Vanda coerulea***)

Prized in cultivation as one of the few blue orchids, the blue vanda has blue, mauve or pinkish flowers. It grows in the hills of northern Burma and neighbouring parts of India but is now very rare in the wild.

Wedding flowers

Coelogyne cristata (see right) is an epiphytic orchid from the eastern Himalayas. Its egg-shaped pseudobulbs shrivel as the plant uses up its food reserves during the cool, dry winter. The pure white flowers appear in spring and are picked for weddings in northern India.

TROPICAL ASIA & AUSTRALIA

Tropical Asia includes most of India and Burma, Thailand, Malaysia, Cambodia and Vietnam. Beyond this lie the huge islands of the Philippines, Borneo and New Guinea, and the 2000 islands of Indonesia. The whole area is in the tropical zone and abounds with orchids. The majority grow as epiphytes in tropical forests, but some mountain species grow on the ground among the rocks and mosses.

Just south of New Guinea is the world's largest island – Australia.

The north is tropical and has epiphytic orchids. Further south, the climate is drier and cooler. The orchids here are terrestrial and become dormant to escape the worst weather. They include some of the most interesting of all orchids. The islands of New Zealand, to the east of Australia, are not as dry and have large areas of forest, with orchids that like cool, moist conditions. The orchids of the South Island of New Zealand grow in grasslands and can stand high levels of light.

Greenhoods
Greenhoods are inconspicuous but interesting orchids. This one (*Pterostylis nutans*, see right) is from north-east New South Wales in Australia. Its slender stems and greenish-pink flowers are hard to see among the surrounding grasses. As many as 95 different kinds of greenhood are found in Australasia and New Guinea.

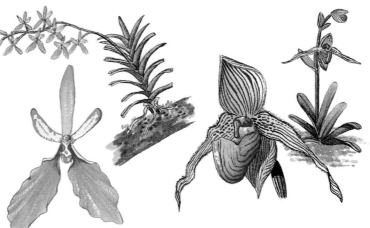

Moth orchid
(*Phalaenopsis schilleriana*)

The thick leathery leaves of this epiphyte are mottled with silver-grey and have purple undersides. It produces huge branched sprays of pale pink flowers which hang down from the trees.

Renanthera imschootiana

This is one of several *Renanthera* orchids that grow in tropical Asia. They are tall, upright epiphytes or climbers with two rows of leathery leaves and spikes of red and yellow flowers.

Paphiopedilum rothschildianum

This is one of the rarest of the tropical slipper orchids. It has leaves 60 centimetres long and tall stems with up to 6 flowers that reach 15 – 25 centimetres across. It grows only on Mount Kinabalu in Borneo.

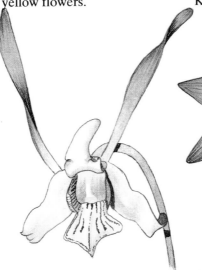

Foxtail orchid
(*Rhynchostylis gigantea*)

This is a large epiphyte from Burma and Thailand, with leaves about 30 centimetres long. The white, pink or purple flowers are 2.5 centimetres across and are clustered around the stem, which hangs down like a tail.

Antelope orchid
(*Dendrobium antennatum*)

The twisted petals of this orchid look like the horns of an antelope. Up to 10 flowers, each about 7 centimetres long, are produced on stems 60 – 90 centimetres tall. It grows as an epiphyte in the rainforests of New Guinea.

Sun orchid
(*Thelymitra ixioides*)

Sun orchids are found in grassland in Australia and New Zealand. The flowers open fully only in bright sunshine. Unlike most orchids, the lip is almost the same as the other petals. This is one of the few really blue orchids.

LEAVES, STEMS AND ROOTS

Most of the food needed by an orchid plant is made inside the leaves by a process known as **photosynthesis**, a word that means "making with light". The leaf contains water, taken in by the roots, and a green chemical called **chlorophyll**. It also receives carbon dioxide gas from the air, which enters through pores or **stomata** in the surface of the leaf. When light falls on the leaf, it provides energy for the chlorophyll to turn the water and carbon dioxide into sugars that feed the plant. As this happens, oxygen is produced which leaves the leaf through the stomata. Photosynthesis stops at night.

How does an orchid grow?

Orchids grow in one of two ways, depending on the genus. Most orchids have **sympodial** (feet-together) growth with a main stem or rhizome that produces a new side-growth each season, followed by another the following year, and so on. They can form clumps or a creeping mass. The flowers appear from the side or the top of the growth.

Monopodial (one-foot) growers have a main stem that continues to lengthen every year as the leaves form on each side. Flowers appear from between the leaf bases.

Storing food

During very hot, dry or cold weather, orchids cannot grow. Instead, they become dormant. They live on food which has been stored in the growing season, using it to start growing again when warm damp weather returns. Food is stored in a special part of the plant.

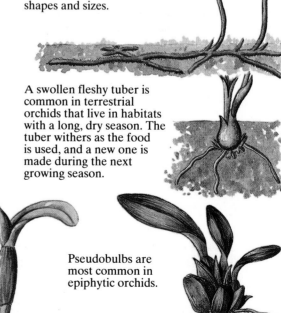

Underground rhizomes are common in terrestrial orchids and can be all shapes and sizes.

A swollen fleshy tuber is common in terrestrial orchids that live in habitats with a long, dry season. The tuber withers as the food is used, and a new one is made during the next growing season.

Pseudobulbs are most common in epiphytic orchids.

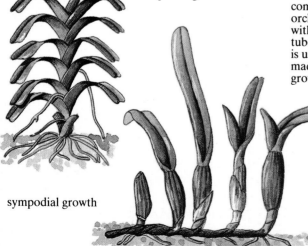

monopodial growth

sympodial growth

Leaf shapes and patterns

Orchid leaves grow alternately on either side of the stem. They are mostly strap-shaped, grass-like or roughly oval. Most tropical species have leathery evergreen leaves that last for several years. Temperate species often have thinner deciduous leaves which die and are shed at the end of each growing season.

Some orchids have patterned leaves. Spotted leaves are common in European *Orchis*. Several Asian slipper orchids (*Paphiopedilum*) have dark markings on their leaves.

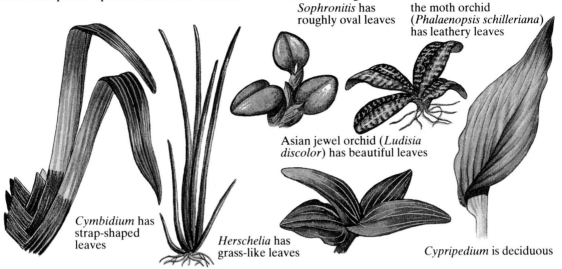

Sophronitis has roughly oval leaves

the moth orchid (*Phalaenopsis schilleriana*) has leathery leaves

Asian jewel orchid (*Ludisia discolor*) has beautiful leaves

Cymbidium has strap-shaped leaves

Herschelia has grass-like leaves

Cypripedium is deciduous

Roots

Roots hold the plant in its place and supply it with water. Terrestrial orchids have underground roots that take in water from the soil. Epiphytes have aerial roots that attach the plant to a tree or a rock and reach out into the air. They take in rainwater as it falls. Dicotyledons develop a tap root and a finely branched system of tapering roots. In monocotyledons like orchids, the roots are an even thickness and seldom branch. They appear directly from the stem.

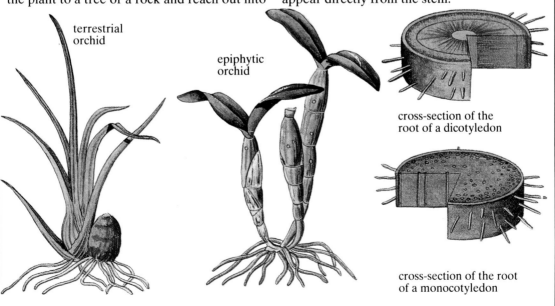

terrestrial orchid

epiphytic orchid

cross-section of the root of a dicotyledon

cross-section of the root of a monocotyledon

THE ORCHID FLOWER

Flowering plants produce flowers in order to make seeds that will grow into new plants. The most noticeable parts of a flower are the petals and sepals. These surround the small sex organs which make up the centre of the flower. The sexual parts consist of a male **anther**, which produces pollen grains, and a female **stigma**. The stigma leads into a chamber (the **ovary**) containing the eggs or **ovules**.

In most flowering plants, the anthers and stigmas are quite separate. In orchids the anther and stigma combine to form the column. Orchid anthers contain pollen grains in waxy masses or pollinia which are attached to a sticky pad or **viscidium**.

For a flower to make seeds, the pollen must first reach the stigma and then join with or **fertilize** the ovules. In many flowers, pollen is transferred from an anther to a stigma by an insect. Flowers attract insects by having interestingly shaped, coloured or scented petals. Most flowers also "reward" the insect with a drink of sugary **nectar** or a feed of pollen.

Beautiful flowers
Orchids have unusual and often beautiful flowers in an endless variety of shapes, but they all have the same parts (see right). The flowers may be smaller than a pinhead or over 15 centimetres across. Every flower colour is found in orchids – all shades of red, yellow, orange, brown, pink, purple, blue, green, white and almost black. Some orchids have delightful perfumes like lemons and roses, or strong spicy scents, or nasty smells like bad meat. The colours, shape, size and scent of an orchid flower are designed to attract particular insects.

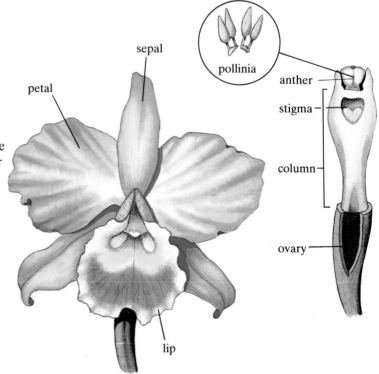

sepal
petal
pollinia
anther
stigma
column
ovary
lip

Spot the lip

However much orchid flowers may vary in colour, shape and size, all have the same basic parts. There are always three sepals and three petals, though sometimes two or all three sepals fuse to form special shapes. The petal that forms the lip is often much larger or smaller than the others and may be held above or below them.

It is the lip that gives orchid flowers their special character. In some species it takes the shape of a tube or a pouch. Others have lips that are frilly, divided into lobes or covered with hairs, warts or crests. The lip may extend backwards to form a tube or spur that is filled with nectar. The lip is often a different colour from the other petals or has markings to attract and guide the insect into the centre of the flower.

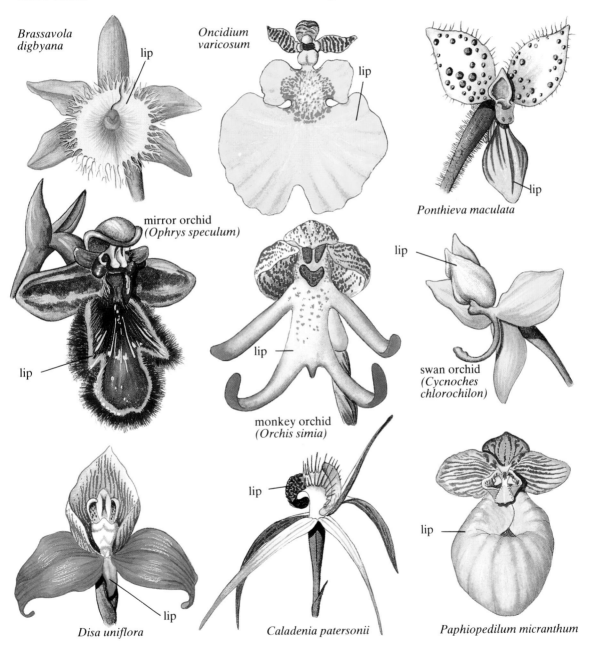

Brassavola digbyana

lip

Oncidium varicosum

lip

Ponthieva maculata

lip

mirror orchid
(*Ophrys speculum*)

lip

lip

lip

monkey orchid
(*Orchis simia*)

lip

swan orchid
(*Cycnoches chlorochilon*)

lip

Disa uniflora

lip

lip

Caladenia patersonii

lip

lip

Paphiopedilum micranthum

POLLINATION

The transfer of pollen from the anther to the stigma is called **pollination**. Insects that do this are known as pollinators. For the ovules to be fertilized and develop into seeds, the pollen must be from the same kind of flower. If the pollen comes from the same kind of flower, but from a different plant, it is called **cross-pollination**. In orchids, cross-pollination is nearly always carried out by insects. If the pollen goes from the anthers to the stigmas of flowers on the same plant, it is called **self-pollination**. Some orchids are naturally self-pollinating when there are no insects around to cross-pollinate them.

Night flowers
Many orchids are night-flowering and pollinated by moths. A sweet, soapy scent is produced at dusk to attract moths. The flowers are white or pale so that they show up in the dark. Some night-flowering orchids have very long nectar spurs. The longest is in the Madagascan comet orchid (*Angraecum sesquipedale*, see below) which measures 30 centimetres. Only one kind of moth has a tongue or proboscis long enough to reach the nectar and pollinate the flower.

Trick or treat?
Orchids are well-known for having the most complex of all flowers. They have developed many devices to attract pollinators. Some orchid flowers give the insect a reward, such as nectar, but others play clever tricks on insects to make sure that they carry out pollination.

Catasetum pileatum, the national flower of Venezuela, has triggers on the column. When an insect touches them, the pollinia shoot out with great force and stick to the insect's body. The insect is so alarmed that it flies off to another plant, where it leaves the pollinia on a stigma.

Trapped!

The Australian greenhood (*Pterostylis grandiflora*, see right) has fused sepals and side petals that form a hooded funnel around the lip and sexual organs. When a fly touches the lip, it springs back and traps the insect inside the chamber. The only way out is past the anther, where it picks up the pollinia before flying to another flower.

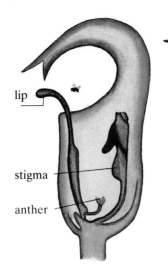

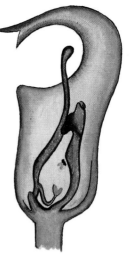

lip

stigma

anther

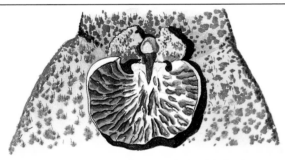

The lip of *Dracula bella* from Colombia looks exactly like the white underside of fungus. It attracts fungus gnats which are fooled into laying eggs on the flower, pollinating it as they do so.

Ophrys orchids have flowers that look and smell like female bees or wasps. The male bee or wasp thinks the flower is a female and tries to mate with it. As he does so, the pollinia stick to his body.

The lip of the American grass pink (*Calopogon pulchellus*) is covered with yellow hairs that look like the anthers of flowering plants. When a bee lands to feed, the lip tips over and sends the bee sliding on to the anther, where the pollinia stick to it.

Some *Oncidium* orchids produce long, branched sprays of flowers that move in the breeze. A certain kind of bee mistakes these flowers for intruders and attacks them to defend its territory. When it charges into a flower, the pollinia stick to its head.

SEEDS AND GERMINATION

An unfertilized orchid flower can open and close within a few days or remain perfect for two months or more, depending on the species. A fertilized flower, however, soon begins to change. The sepals and petals that attracted the pollinator are no longer needed, so they either fade and wither or turn green to protect the ovary. As the seeds develop, the ovary enlarges into a seed pod. Some orchid seed pods ripen within a few weeks, others take many months. When the pod is ripe, it splits open and the seeds are carried away by the wind.

Hundreds and thousands
Orchid seeds are as fine as dust and even a small pod contains hundreds of thousands. Some tropical orchids produce very large pods that hold as many as 3 million seeds (see below). With these numbers, why are orchids so rare? The answers are that some tropical orchids very rarely set seed and that the seeds seldom land in a suitable growing place. Only one or two of those seeds will grow into new plants that will survive well enough to produce their own seed.

How seed pods develop
The pictures below show how the seed pods of *Cattleya* develop.

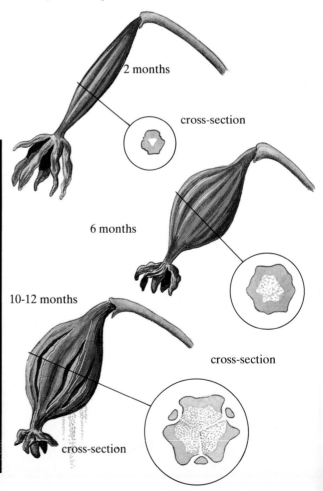

2 months

cross-section

6 months

10-12 months

cross-section

cross-section

Orchid life-cycle

An orchid seed has no food store. Instead, it relies on finding a special **fungus** with which to live and feed. As soon as the seed becomes damp, it splits and starts to grow into a new plant. If there is no fungus present at this point, the seed dies. If a seed and fungus do join together, it is not necessarily the end of the problem. The orchid and fungus both feed from each other. If one becomes much stronger than the other, it can lead to death. However, if they give and take equally, a partnership or **mycorrhiza** is formed that helps them both to grow. At first the fungus sends fine threads (**hyphae**) into the germinating seed. These later extend into the roots and other underground parts of the orchid. The fungus obtains its food by sending other hyphae into dead and decaying plant material.

The tiny orchid seedling grows very slowly. To start with, it is not recognizable as a plant, being just a miniature rhizome or protocorm. As it grows larger and stronger, a shoot and roots develop. Eventually, the seedling sends out its first leaf and begins to photosynthesize. The plant can now make some of its own food, though it still partly relies on the fungus. An orchid may take many years to reach flowering size from seed. In some European terrestrial species, it may take as long as 15 years.

Life-cycle of Mediterranean bee orchid (*Ophrys*)

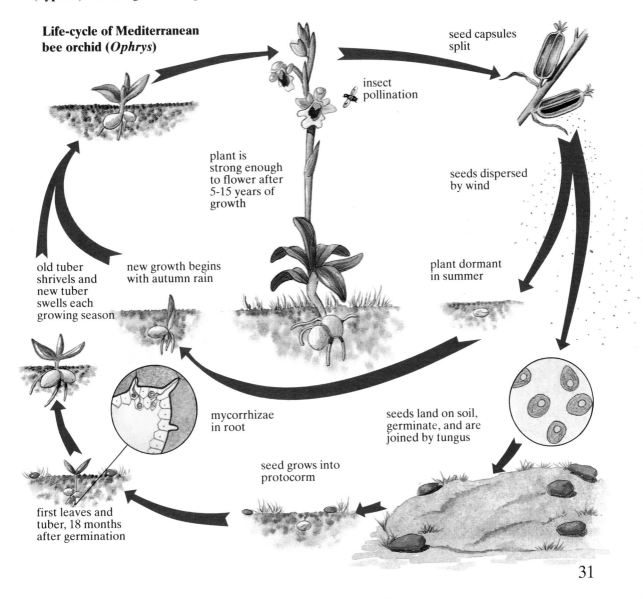

seed capsules split

insect pollination

plant is strong enough to flower after 5-15 years of growth

seeds dispersed by wind

old tuber shrivels and new tuber swells each growing season

new growth begins with autumn rain

plant dormant in summer

mycorrhizae in root

seeds land on soil, germinate, and are joined by fungus

seed grows into protocorm

first leaves and tuber, 18 months after germination

31

ORCHID SAPROPHYTES

Some plants have no leaves and do not contain chlorophyll so they cannot make their own food by photosynthesis. They must therefore obtain food in other ways. Some plants called **saprophytes** are adapted to feed directly on plant remains, such as decaying leaves. Others form a partnership with a fungus that feeds them by breaking down dead matter. Most saprophytes are fungi or **bacteria** (microscopic living things). Orchids are one of the few families of flowering plants that has saprophytic species.

All orchids depend on a fungus for food until they are large enough to produce leaves (see p. 31). Some terrestrial orchids revert to saprophytic feeding if growing conditions are poor. They can remain underground for several seasons. However, some are saprophytes throughout their lives and never have any green parts.

Saprophytes can grow in places that are too dark for photosynthesis. Saprophytic orchids are common in dark, dense forests where the leaves block out most of the light. Forests also have moist soil with plenty of dead leaves for the saprophytes to feed on. Little is known about saprophytic orchids as they are impossible to cultivate.

Partial saprophytes

Some orchids are leafless but not entirely saprophytic because they have chlorophyll in other parts. An example is the coral root orchid (*Corallorhiza trifida*, see below), which has green flower stalks and ovaries. It can therefore make a little of its food by photosynthesis.

The ghost orchid or frog orchid (*Polyrrhiza lindenii*, see below), a leafless partial saprophyte, can photosynthesize through the long aerial greenish-grey roots which contain chlorophyll.

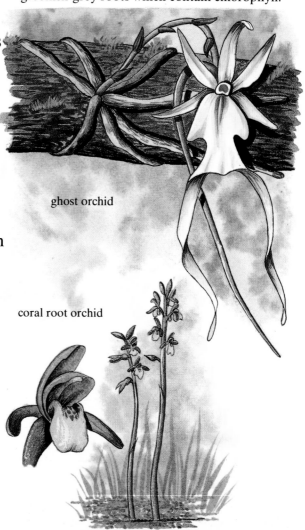

ghost orchid

coral root orchid

Life underground

The spurred coral-root or ghost orchid (*Epipogium aphyllum*) lives entirely underground, apart from when flowers are produced. Instead of roots, it has a branched rhizome covered with fine hairs and mycorrhizal fungus.

The Australian *Rhizanthella gardneri* is very strange – it grows and flowers underground. Only its seed pods push up to the surface so that the seeds can be dispersed.

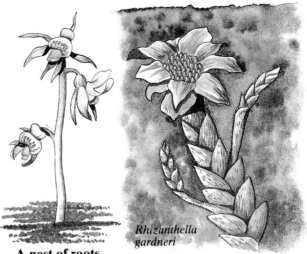

spurred
coral-root

Rhizanthella gardneri

Violet beauty

The violet limodore (*Limodorum abortivum*, see below) is a saprophyte. It has purple stalks, up to 80 centimetres tall, with violet (sometimes white) flowers. It grows mainly in the Mediterranean and is always found near pine trees.

A nest of roots

The Bird's nest orchid (*Neottia nidus-avis*, see below) has dense and tangled roots that resemble a bird's nest. The flowers and stalks are pale brown and from a distance they look dead. It grows in dense woods, especially pine or beech, throughout central and northern Europe and Asia, as far as Japan.

EPIPHYTIC ORCHIDS

An epiphyte is a plant that grows on the surface of another plant – usually on the bark of a tree or shrub – instead of in the soil. It clings on with its roots but is otherwise independent, making its own food by photosynthesis. Epiphytes can also grow on rocks and artificial structures, such as fences and telegraph poles. Those that grow on rocks are called lithophytes.

Over half of the world's orchids are epiphytes. Most live in dense tropical forests where it is too dark to grow on the ground or where a small orchid cannot compete with the many large plants. The richest forests of all for epiphytes are those that grow on the sides of mountains. They are called cloud forests because they are cooler and constantly bathed in mist and cloud.

Perching up in trees has a number of advantages. There is more light for photosynthesis and more insects for pollination. There is also more wind so the dust-like seed can be blown long distances. However, it has disadvantages too. The worst problem is drying out in the sun and wind. Epiphytic plants have special ways of making the most of rain, dew and humidity, and can go without water for long periods.

Special roots

Epiphytes have thick aerial roots which are silvery greenish-grey (see right). The green colouring is chlorophyll, so the roots can make a little food by photosynthesis. When the roots come in contact with a surface, they cling tightly. The silvery outer layer or **velamen** consists of air-filled cells that help to protect the plant and feed it. The velamen reflects heat and light, and acts like a sponge to soak up moisture. Some of the roots grow out into the air or grow upwards like spikes, trapping dead leaves which feed the plant as they decay.

Tough leaves

The leaves of epiphytes are tough and leathery to resist drying by sun and wind. Some species also have specially shaped leaves to protect against wind damage and cut down on water loss.

The stomata of some species only open at night to take in carbon dioxide. The gas is then stored in the leaf for use in photosynthesis the next day. Keeping the stomata closed during the hot, dry daylight hours reduces moisture loss.

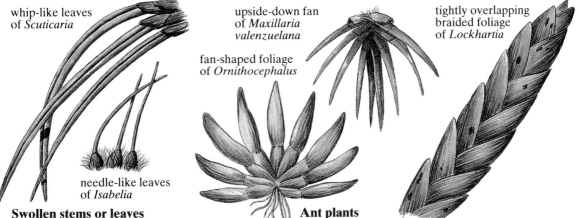

whip-like leaves of *Scuticaria*

needle-like leaves of *Isabelia*

upside-down fan of *Maxillaria valenzuelana*

fan-shaped foliage of *Ornithocephalus*

tightly overlapping braided foliage of *Lockhartia*

Swollen stems or leaves

Most epiphytic orchids store water in swollen stems or pseudobulbs (see below) so that the plant can survive long, dry periods. They shrivel as the water is used up and swell up again when it rains. Some species do not have pseudobulbs. Instead, they store water in fleshy leaves. The leaves of the Australian cucumber orchid (*Dendrobium cucumerinum*) look like gherkins.

Ant plants

Some epiphytes have special parts in which ants live. For example, some *Schomburgkia* orchids (see below), which grow in tropical America and the West Indies, have hollow pseudobulbs up to 90 centimetres long. Ants build their colonies in them. The ants keep the leaves clean and defend the plant against insect pests and browsing animals. In return, the plant gives them shelter and rewards them with nectar.

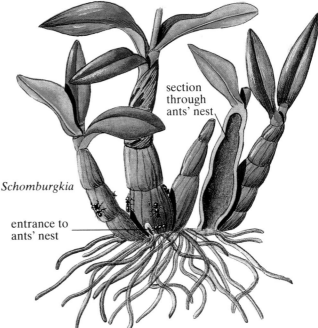

section through ants' nest

Schomburgkia

entrance to ants' nest

ORCHID COLLECTORS

Wild orchids in their natural habitats are a beautiful sight and exciting to find. Since the 16th century explorers and collectors have travelled all over the Earth, bringing back many exotic plants to grow in greenhouses and gardens.

The cultivation of orchids began in Europe during the 17th century. The first tropical orchid to flower in Europe was the Central American *Brassavola nodosa* in 1685. During the 18th century, more and more orchids were introduced, but few survived because no one understood how to grow them. By the 19th century, growers had discovered what tropical orchids need in the way of warmth and moisture and began designing special greenhouses for them. Collectors travelled all over the world. Many took every orchid that they could find to prevent rivals from searching the same place. This led to many species becoming rare or extinct (dying out) as soon as they were discovered.

Orchids are now grown by specialist growers in nurseries, rather than being collected from the wild. With cheap greenhouses and heated homes, all orchid lovers can now grow these exciting plants.

Chance arrivals
Some tropical orchids arrived in Europe quite by chance. In the 19th century a man named William Cattley received a parcel from Brazil. He did not recognize the plant stems that were used as packing material, so he planted some of them. He was amazed when, in 1818, they produced huge mauve flowers. The orchid (shown right) was named *Cattleya labiata* after him.

The Chatsworth collection

The Duke of Devonshire (see right) began collecting orchids in the 1830s. Within 10 years he had the finest collection in Great Britain and had built a magnificent conservatory on his estate at Chatsworth to display his plants. *Dendrobium devonianum*, known in the time of Queen Victoria as the "King of Dendrobiums", was named after the Duke when it was introduced from the Himalayas in 1837.

The "Orchid King"

The leading orchid nursery in the 1880s belonged to Frederick Sander, "the Orchid King". He had vast ranges of glasshouses in England, Belgium and the United States, with about 20 collectors working in tropical regions to bring back orchids. He was made Royal Orchid Grower by Queen Victoria and one of the finest orchids from the Philippines, *Euanthe sanderiana* (see below), was named after him.

A veteran orchid hunter

Benedict Roezl worked as a collector for over 40 years, travelling on foot throughout the whole of tropical America. His success was partly due to the fact that he had lost his left hand in an accident and wore an iron hook. The Indian tribes he met were so amazed by this hook that they did not harm him. His name was given to the pansy orchid, *Miltonia roezlii* (see below) which grows in Colombia and Panama.

ORCHIDS UNDER THREAT

Wild plants can become very rare for many reasons. One of the main causes is collecting plants for cultivation. If too many are dug up or their flowers are picked, there may not be enough plants left in the wild to reproduce and increase the population. Another important cause is loss of habitats. This happens when wild places are cleared for farming, building and roads, or when forests are cut down.

The plants worst affected are those that are slow-growing and found only in a few places. For this reason, orchids are among the most endangered plants. It is thought that 10 per cent of all wild plants are now rare or under threat. Many of these are orchids.

In 1973 the CITES agreement – the Convention on International Trade in Endangered Species of Wild Fauna and Flora – was made to prevent the trade in wild plants and animals. Conservation groups also work to save tropical forests and other wild places where orchids live. Recently, nature reserves have been created to protect orchids and their habitats.

Disappearing bogs

Bog orchids (*Hammarbya paludosa*) grow throughout northern Europe in peat bogs, one of Europe's most threatened habitats. As these are drained for agriculture or cut to provide peat for potting compost and fuel for burning, so more and more orchids are lost. The bog orchid is only 5 – 12 centimetres tall. Like tropical orchids, it has pseudobulbs. It also produces tiny buds at the tips of each leaf which drop off and grow into new plants.

Orchids under threat

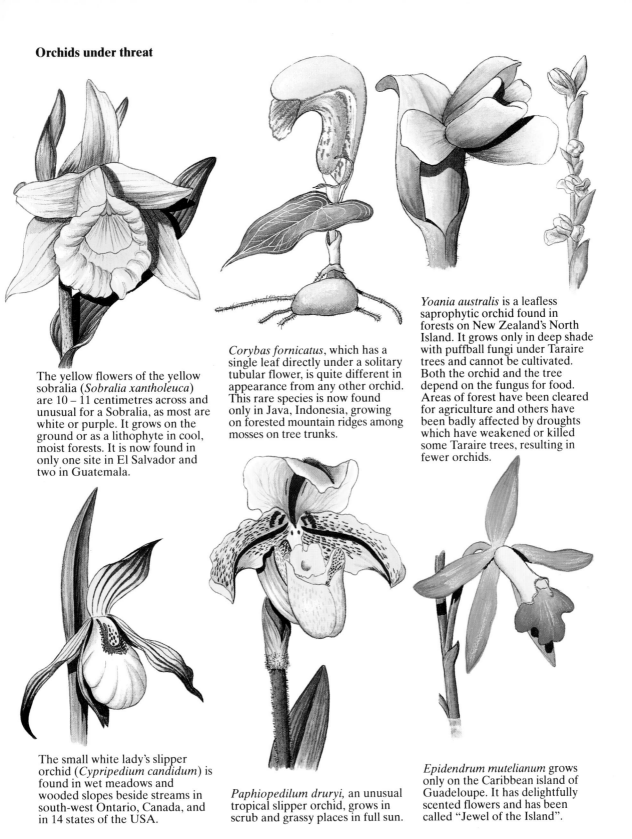

The yellow flowers of the yellow sobralia (*Sobralia xantholeuca*) are 10 – 11 centimetres across and unusual for a Sobralia, as most are white or purple. It grows on the ground or as a lithophyte in cool, moist forests. It is now found in only one site in El Salvador and two in Guatemala.

Corybas fornicatus, which has a single leaf directly under a solitary tubular flower, is quite different in appearance from any other orchid. This rare species is now found only in Java, Indonesia, growing on forested mountain ridges among mosses on tree trunks.

Yoania australis is a leafless saprophytic orchid found in forests on New Zealand's North Island. It grows only in deep shade with puffball fungi under Taraire trees and cannot be cultivated. Both the orchid and the tree depend on the fungus for food. Areas of forest have been cleared for agriculture and others have been badly affected by droughts which have weakened or killed some Taraire trees, resulting in fewer orchids.

The small white lady's slipper orchid (*Cypripedium candidum*) is found in wet meadows and wooded slopes beside streams in south-west Ontario, Canada, and in 14 states of the USA.

Paphiopedilum druryi, an unusual tropical slipper orchid, grows in scrub and grassy places in full sun.

Epidendrum mutelianum grows only on the Caribbean island of Guadeloupe. It has delightfully scented flowers and has been called "Jewel of the Island".

BREEDING & CULTIVATION

Compared with most flowering plants, orchids are difficult to grow because they need special conditions. It is even more difficult to raise orchids from seed.

As orchid seeds have no food stores and need fungus to help them grow, they cannot be sown like other seeds. Instead, they are grown in laboratories in special containers with particular plant foods. However, growing orchids from seed is not the only way of making new plants. In the 1960s, a new method – tissue culture or micropropagation – was developed. This is also done in a laboratory. A few cells from the growing point of a plant are removed and grown in the same way as the seeds. As the cells grow, they produce a protocorm which develops into several new plants.

New plants raised from seeds (breeding) may vary in appearance, resembling the parent plants in different ways. Plants reproduced by tissue culture are all identical to the plant that provided the cells for culture. Breeding is done to produce new and exciting flowers, while tissue culture is used to reproduce rare or very beautiful orchids.

Growing orchids
Most cultivated orchids are tropical epiphytes and need a special compost made from bark chippings. If they were grown in soil, the aerial roots would rot. Tropical epiphytes must be watered and sprayed with luke-warm rainwater and have fresh, damp air. The amount of warmth needed will depend on the kind of orchid. Certain epiphytic orchids will grow as houseplants but most do best in a greenhouse.

What is a hybrid?

In the wild, seed is normally produced by parents from the same species. In cultivation, seed can be produced by using parents from different but closely related species. The pollen from one plant is placed on the stigma of the other. Any new plant raised from their seed is called a **hybrid**. It is often stronger than its parents with flowers a mixture of them both.

Hybrids have special names given by the breeder. The first orchid hybrid to flower (in 1856) was called *Calanthe* Dominyi, after its breeder, John Dominy. Its parents were two species, *Calanthe furcata* and *Calanthe masuca*, written as *Calanthe furcata* x *C. masuca*.

Orchids are among the few flowering plants in which hybrids can also be produced using parents from different genera. This is because many orchid genera are very closely related and so very similar. Such hybrids are called **intergeneric hybrids**. This means that many unusual orchids can be grown.

Intergeneric hybrids have names that combine those of the two genera used, or, if there are more than two, a different name ending in 'ara'. An *Odontoglossum* crossed with a *Cochlioda* gives an *Odontioda*. However, a hybrid of *Odontoglossum*, *Cochlioda* and *Miltonia* is called a *Vuylstekeara*, after a Belgian grower, Charles Vuylsteke.

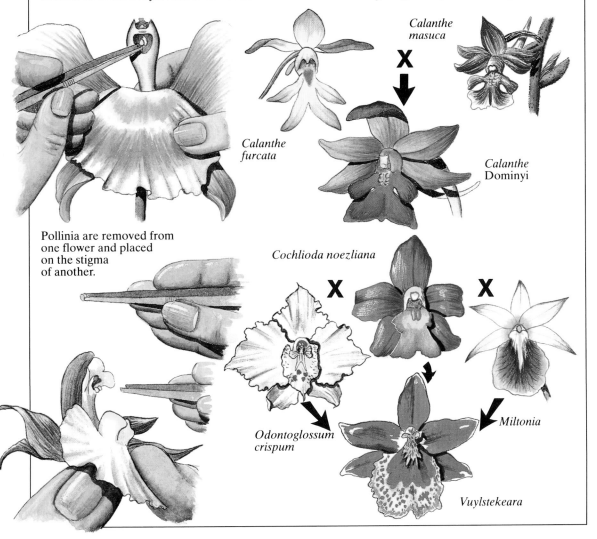

Pollinia are removed from one flower and placed on the stigma of another.

Calanthe furcata

Calanthe masuca

Calanthe Dominyi

Cochlioda noezliana

Odontoglossum crispum

Miltonia

Vuylstekeara

USEFUL ORCHIDS

For such a large family, orchids have surprisingly few uses other than in horticulture. Several are used on a small scale as foods and for flavouring. In the Seychelles, tea is made from orchid leaves, and in the Middle East a starchy substance known as salep is obtained from orchid tubers for use in food and medicines. An oil from orchids can be used in cosmetics, but the only orchid grown on a large scale for practical purposes is vanilla. Its pods are used as a flavouring in the food industry and as a scent in perfumes.

Orchids are among the most valuable of all flowering plants as ornamental plants and cut flowers. In the mid-1900s, plants were sold for hundreds, or even thousands of pounds each. They cost less today mainly because of micropropagation (see p. 40). There are orchid nurseries throughout Europe and the United States, as well as in Australia, New Zealand, South Africa, Japan, Brazil, the Philippines and Thailand. Those in tropical countries produce vast numbers of orchid blooms for florists, sending them worldwide by air.

Orchid flavour?
Wild vanilla (*Vanilla planifolia*) orchids grow in Central America. Vanilla flavouring comes from the long thin pods which are picked green and fermented in airtight boxes until they turn black. It is used in chocolate, ice-cream, desserts and other sweet foods. There are vanilla plantations in many parts of the tropics, including Mexico, the West Indies, Polynesia and the Seychelles. Vanilla orchids are vigorous climbers, reaching 15 metres. The green flowers have to be pollinated by hand in order for pods to form.

Cooktown orchid (*Dendrobium biggibum*)

This species and the similar *D. phalaenopsis* grow wild in Northern Queensland, Australia. They are widely used for breeding pompadour dendrobiums, which are very popular cut flowers. Exported mainly from Thailand, they come in various shades of mauve, pink and purple, as well as a greenish-white, and last 6 weeks in water.

Traditional medicines

Some orchids are used to produce natural medicines.

The rhizome and roots of the nerve root or American valerian (*Cypripedium pubescens*) are used to make a medicine to treat nervous tension and sleeplessness. The uses of this plant were learnt from native North American Indians. They valued it as a sedative long before European settlers reached the continent.

Bletilla striata, known as thousand-year palm in China, is a ground-dwelling orchid from China and Japan. It is popular in cultivation, having attractive purple flowers on stems 30 – 60 centimetres tall. The pseudobulbs grow under the soil. They are used in Chinese medicines to stop internal bleeding or mixed with oil to treat burns and skin problems.

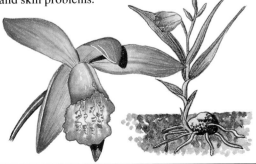

Flour orchids

The tubers of this early purple orchid (*Orchis mascula*, see below) and a number of other *Orchis* species are dried and ground into flour, known as salep. It is used to make invalid foods and medicines. At one time it was popular as a hot winter drink and was sold in the streets of cities such as London and Istanbul. Salep is seldom made nowadays because so many of these orchids are becoming rare.

GLOSSARY

ANGIOSPERM – A plant with flowers and seeds that grow inside a fruit.

ANTHER – The part of a stamen that produces pollen.

BACTERIA (singular bacterium) – Microscopic living things with only one cell.

CHLOROPHYLL – The green pigment in plants that traps the energy of sunlight for photosynthesis.

CROSS-POLLINATION – The transfer of pollen from the anthers of one flower to the stigma of the same kind of flower on a different plant.

COLUMN – The sex organ of an orchid flower, in which the anther and stigma are combined.

DORMANT – Alive but resting, with no sign of growth.

EPIPHYTE – A plant that grows on the surface of another plant but uses it only for support.

FERTILIZE – The joining of an ovule with a male pollen grain.

FUNGUS (plural fungi) – A living thing, rather like a plant, that obtains its food from dead or living animals and plants. It reproduces by spores which in some fungi are contained in growths known as toadstools.

GENUS (plural genera) – A group of closely related species within a family.

HABITAT – The place where a plant or animal lives in the wild.

HYBRID – A living thing whose parents belong to different species.

HYPHAE (singular hypha) – The thread-like parts of a fungus.

INTERGENERIC HYBRID – A hybrid made by cross-pollinating species of different genera.

LIP – One of three petals in an orchid flower that is different from the other two.

MONOPODIAL – The way a plant grows by lengthening the main stem or rhizome.

MYCORRHIZA (plural mycorrhizae) – A partnership between the roots of a plant and the hyphae of a fungus that helps them both to grow.

NECTAR – A sugary liquid produced by flowers.

OVARY – The part of the flower containing ovules.

OVULE – The egg inside the female part of a flower.

PETALS – The parts of the flower that are protected by the sepals.

PHOTOSYNTHESIS – The food-making process in green plants, in which the energy of sunlight is used to turn carbon dioxide and water into sugars and oxygen, which is released.

POLLEN – The male cell that fertilizes an ovule to make seed.

POLLINATION – The carrying of pollen from the male parts of a flower to the female parts.

POLLINIA (singular pollinium) – Masses of pollen grains joined together.

PSEUDOBULB – A swelling at the base of the stem in which epiphytic orchids store food.

RHIZOME – A thick stem that grows along under the surface of the soil and produces new growths.

SAPROPHYTE – A living thing that feeds on dead matter.

SEED – A fully grown fertilized ovule that can grow into a new plant.

SELF-POLLINATION – The transfer of pollen from the anthers of one flower to the stigma of another flower on the same plant.

SEPALS – The leaf-like outer parts of a flower that protect the petals before the bud opens.

SPECIES – A group of individuals within a genus that are capable of interbreeding.

STIGMA – The part of the flower on which the pollen lands.

STOMATA (singular stoma) – The pores in a leaf through which carbon dioxide enters and oxygen and water vapour leave.

SYMPODIAL – The way a plant grows by producing side branches instead of lengthening the main stem or rhizome.

TUBER – A swollen stem or root that stores food.

VELAMEN – The outer layer of cells in an aerial root that absorbs moisture.

VISCIDIUM – A sticky pad that attaches the pollinia to an insect as it visits the flower.

FURTHER READING

For children

The Open Book of Plant Life edited by Carol Richardson; Hodder & Stoughton, 1981.

Plant (Eyewitness Guide) by David Burnie; Dorling Kindersley, 1989.

For adults

Wild Flowers of the World by Barbara Everard and Brian Morley; Octopus, 1974.

Wild Orchids of Britain and Europe by P. & J. Davies and Anthony Huxley; Chatto & Windus, 1983.

INDEX